Carnavalet Museum

GENERAL GUIDE

MUSEE
CARNAVALET

Summary

Introduction

The Carnavalet museum gets its name from one of the two historic town houses in which it is located, in the heart of the Marais quarter of Paris. It is one of the fifteen museums belonging to the Ville de Paris. and aims to illustrate, in a variety of ways, the history of Paris from its origins to the present day, with objects unearthed in the course of archaeological digs, or salvaged through conservation or rescue operations, works of art and documents showing the city's development over the centuries and its most famous sons and daughters, and items of decoration and furniture epitomising the evolution of the Parisian home.

The ever-expanding collections, many of which could not even be shown, owing to lack of space, posed a problem which was only resolved by converting an adjoining building, the hôtel Le Peletier de Saint-Fargeau. The restoration and conversion of the house, which began in 1984, were completed in July 1989, when it was opened to visitors as part of the Carnavalet museum. A gallery crosses the lycée Victor Hugo on the first floor, linking the two houses, so that they can both be taken in on a single visit. The visitors' entrance and exit are both situated at 23, rue de Sévigné.

Courtyard of the Hôtel Carnavalet

The collections relating to the history of Paris from its origins to 1789 are to be found in the hôtel Carnavalet, where the temporary exhibitions are also held. The hôtel Le Peletier de Saint-Fargeau covers the period from 1789 to the present day and also houses the museum's auditorium, the Graphic Arts room, which is open to researchers on request (entrance situated at 29, rue de Sévigné), and the various technical departments.

The purpose of this brief guidebook is to provide the visitor with a logical and rewarding tour of the Carnavalet museum as a whole. The various sections of the museum are described individually and in greater detail in other guides, albums and catalogues.

PLAN OF THE HÔTEL CARNAVALET

**Paris from its origins
to the end of the Middle Ages**
1 Prehistory
2 Lutetia (Gallo-Roman)
3 The Early Middle Ages
4 The Middle Ages

**Paris in the XVIth century
and under Henri IV**
5 Passage (Jean Goujon's *Saisons*)
6 Passage (Berton's *retable*)
7 The Ligneris gallery
8 The Catherine de Médicis gallery
9 The Henri IV gallery
10 The Blue gallery (engravings)

**Paris during the reigns of Louis XIII
and Louis XIV and the Regency period**
11 The Sévigné staircase
12 and 13 Paris under Louis XIII
and before the coming-of-age of
Louis XIV
14 Paris in the XVIIth century
(engravings)

15 Paris under Louis XIV
16 wooden panelling from the
Pitié hospital
17 Drawing-room of the hôtel Colbert
de Villacerf
18 Passages : sketches on religious themes
19 Main drawing-room of the hôtel
de la Rivière
20 Main bedroom of the hôtel de la
Rivière
21 The Sévigné gallery
22 The Regency period
23 Collection of china.

**The municipality
in Paris under the Ancien Régime**
24,25 and 26

**Paris as it looked before 1760, under
Louis XV**
27 The Grevenbrœk gallery
28 Small salon Louis XV
29 The Raguenet gallery

Groundfloor

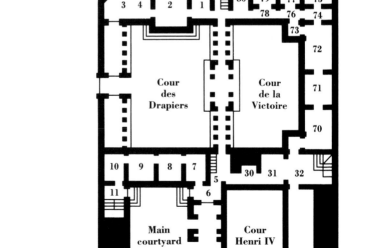

Hôtel Carnavalet

1st floor

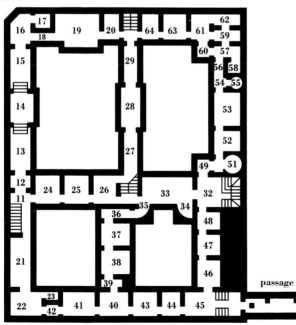

Plan of the Hôtel
Le Peletier de Saint-Fargeau

The French Revolution
101 The States General
102 The Bastille
103 Federation Day
104 From the monarchy to the republic
105 The royal family
106 The Temple
108 The Convention/The Terror
109 Thermidor/The Directory
110 The War
111 Vandalism and conservation
112 Le Sueur
113 Porcelain

Paris in the first half of the XIXth century, from the Consulate to the Second Republic
115 The First Empire
116 The Restoration
117 The painters'view of Paris (1800-1850)
118 The painters'view of Paris (1800-1850)
119 July 1830
120 The July monarchy
121 The Second Republic
122 The Romantic movement
124 The Romantic movement
125 The Romantic movement

Paris from the Second Empire to the present day
126 The painters'view of Paris
127 The painters'view of Paris
128 The Second Empire
129 The Second Empire
130 The siege of Paris
131 The Commune
132 The Third Republic
133 The painters'view of Paris
134 Sitting-room
135 The painters'view of Paris
136 The world of literature
137 The Belle Epoque
138 The Belle Epoque
141 The Café de Paris
142 Fouquet's jewellery shop
145 1914-1918
146 The Wendel ballroom
147 The world of literature/ The XXth century

ground-floor

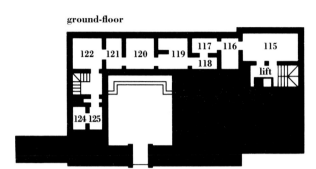

Hôtel Le Peletier de Saint-Fargeau

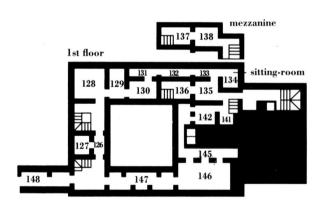

mezzanine

1st floor

sitting-room

2nd floor

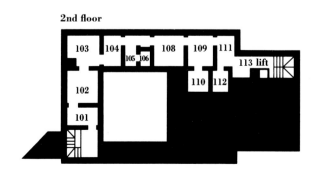

Historical background of the Hôtel Carnavalet

This is one of the most beautiful houses in the Marais and an outstanding example of the all too rare Renaissance mansions still standing in Paris.

It was originally built for Jacques des Ligneris, President of the Paris Parliament, and work began on it in 1548. The master mason Nicolas Dupuis was responsible for this first stage, which seems to have lasted until about 1560. The main part of the house was at that time situated between the courtyard and garden, with a fairly low building running along the rue de la Culture Sainte-Catherine, now renamed the rue de Sévigné; a wing almost entirely composed of arcades opened out on to the South side of the courtyard, flanking the rue des Francs-Bourgeois. Whilst still at the construction stage, the house was adorned with a magnificent decoration, carved in bas-relief, much of which can be attributed to Jean Goujon and his workshop.

The house was acquired in 1578 by Françoise de

Kernevenoc'h or Kernevenoy, the widow of a Breton
gentleman nicknamed Carnavalet. Claude Boislève, a
speculator, bought the mansion in 1654 and decided to
enlarge and modernize it in around 1660. The famous
architect François Mansart was chosen to carry out the work.
He scarcely touched the main building, but made drastic
changes to the South wing and the entrance; he also appears
to have been entirely responsible for the construction of the
North wing. Mansart's additions to the house were
complemented by a beautifully carved decoration, essentially
the work of Gérard van Obstal, which merges perfectly into
the Renaissance parts of the building.

Garden of the Hôtel Carnavalet

Implicated along with the superintendent Fouquet, Boislève was imprisoned in 1662 and his personal property confiscated. The house was rented out to Marie de Rabutin-Chantal, the marquise de Sévigné, who lived there from 1677 until her death in 1696. She was followed by one of the King's secretaries, Brunet de Rancy, who was in turn succeeded by the La Briffe family and finally by the Dupré de Saint-Maur family. The Ponts et Chaussées school took over the premises from 1814 to 1829, and from 1829 to 1866 the building was occupied by various private institutions until the Ville de Paris acquired it in 1866, at the instigation of the baron Haussmann, in order to house its historical collections. The architect Victor Parmentier was chosen to restore the building. The original house was enlarged between 1876 and 1890 to allow room for the museum. Around the garden area, Renaissance-style galleries were erected and three architectural constructions were rebuilt on site. The museum was opened to the public in 1880 and further enlarged between approximately 1907 and 1920.

Since these alterations, the hôtel Carnavalet has been rectangular in shape, the buildings within forming a cross separating four courtyards, three of which are covered with flower-beds.

Paris
from its origins
to 1789

The Renaissance boss portal is still visible in the façade overlooking the rue de Sévigné, inset by Mansart within the composition which encloses the main courtyard.

The bas-reliefs are mid-sixteenth century, and can possibly be attributed to Jean Goujon or to his workshop, apart from the tympanum, which appears to be from a later period. The two figures of Force and Vigilance are by Gérard van Obstal, as is the allegorical bas-relief with its somewhat obscure theme adorning the rue des Francs-Bourgeois side of the façade.

A vaulted porch leads into the main courtyard. As with the exterior façade, Jacques de Ligneris' Renaissance residence is astutely worked into Claude Boislève's "Grand Siècle" mansion. At the far end of the courtyard, the main part of the building has retained its mid-XVIth century aspect, with its mullioned windows on the first floor separated by four large bas-relief figures representing *les Saisons*, an extremely original concept for the time. Behind the façade which looks out on to the street, the XVIth century portal which featured in Mansart's building is adorned by three elegant figures in bas-relief, l'*Autorité* and two *Renommées*, which can certainly be attributed to Jean Goujon. The lower half of the South wing is taken up by the former XVIth century loggia; its arcades, decorated with masks of fauns, were closed off by François Mansart, who built the first floor, its windows separated by four large bas-relief figures personifying the *Elements*, executed by an unknown hand. The North wing, which seems to have been entirely designed by François Mansart, is a reproduction, in broad outline, of the South wing; the four large bas-relief figures situated between the windows on the first floor represent various deities, and were carved by Gérard van Obstal.

The bronze statue of Louis XIV, by Antoine

Van Obstal. Bas-relief, North wing

Coysevox, was placed in the middle of the courtyard in 1890, having been inaugurated on 14th July 1689 at the Hôtel de Ville de Paris, where it remained until the Revolution.

From the reception area, designed and laid out by J.P. Willemotte, one can see the early XXth century Cour Henri IV. On one of the walls of this courtyard is a bronze bas-relief of *Henri IV* on horseback, by Philippe Lemaire, which dates back to 1834. It adorned the façade of the Hôtel de Ville until 1871.

To the left is the Cour des drapiers. This was formerly the garden of the hôtel Carnavalet, now bordered on the East side by the façade of the main building and on the three remaining sides by constructions from the latter half of the XIXth century. These relatively recent additions do, however, include three items of architectural interest salvaged during the demolition of ancient Paris and rebuilt stone by stone: to the South, the archway which used to span the rue de Nazareth in the île de la Cité; to the West, the façade of the office belonging to the corporation of Merchant Drapers, which was near the Halles (XVIIth century); to the North, an overhang from the hôtel des Marets (early XVIIIth century).

Like the adjoining courtyard, the garden is designed "à la française".

BEYOND THE LUYNES STAIRCASE (No. 32) AND THE ROOMS DEVOTED TO THE WOOD PANELLING OF LEDOUX (Nos. 31 AND 30), TO WHICH WE WILL RETURN LATER ON IN THE VISIT, A CORRIDOR LEADS INTO THE ARCADES SEPARATING TWO COURTYARDS, NOW TURNED INTO GARDENS.

PARIS FROM ITS ORIGINS TO THE END OF THE MIDDLE AGES

In these four ground-floor rooms, overlooking the garden, the visitor will be shown a limited and temporary selection of the museum's vast collection of items relating to the origins of Paris and the history of the city up to the XVth century. Most of these objects were unearthed during archaeological digs or demolition work in the capital. A number of relief maps and scale models of buildings are also shown here.

No. 1 - Prehistory and protohistory. Paris soil through the ages : The Paleolithic Age (flint tools, wrought or decorated bone), the Neolithic Age (burnished stone axes, pottery), the Bronze Age (arms and ornamental objects), the era of Halstatt and la Tène, Gallic independence (set of burial items in iron, everyday bronze and pottery objects, gold coins belonging to the Parisii tribe, from which gave Paris gets its name).

Bronze Age. Spearhead

No. 2 - Lutetia. An impression of the Gallo-Roman city as it developed, from the second half of the 1st century B.C. to the end of the IVth century A.D. The town was of only average size, but its position at the crossroads of road and river transport soon ensured its prosperity. Architectonic fragments from public buildings. Steles and burial items, the accidentally-cast mask of a dead child's face. The art of statuary, pottery (sigillated objects), bronze, glassware, jewellery, coins. Scale reconstitutions of the Forum, the Thermes de l'Est at Cluny, the Arènes. The beginnings of Christianity : sarcophagus lids, burial ornaments.

No. 3 - The Early Middle Ages. The Merovingian Age. Paris, capital of Clovis (VIth century). Burial handicraft : stone and plaster sarcophagi with panels decorated in relief motifs. Arms, damascened ornaments,

Second half of VIIth
century. Belt
plate-buckle
in iron damascened
with silver

Gallo-Roman period.
Eros funèbre

PARIS FROM ITS ORIGINS
TO THE END OF THE MIDDLE AGES

jewellery, pottery, gold coins belonging to the Kings of Paris.
The city's importance declined during the Carolingian Age;
arms discovered in the Seine provide a testimonial of the late
IXth century siege of Paris by the Normans.

No. 4 - The Middle Ages. Under the Capetians,
Paris regained its capital status. The city was at its most
radiant under Philippe-Auguste, saint Louis and Charles V,
as one can see from the magnificent buildings of the period.
A number of carvings from monuments are shown here: a
console featuring the figure of an angel (second half of the
XIIth century), found during excavations at the Hôtel-Dieu; a

Gable from the tomb
of Blanche de France,
originally in the
convent des
Cordeliers,
showing her at the
feet
of saint Louis

statue-column (early XIIIth century) which once adorned one of Notre-Dame's portals (found headless in the Seine); a bas-relief from the tomb of Blanche de France, the daughter of saint Louis (mid-XIIIth century), originally in the convent des Cordeliers; a bas-relief from the tomb of Prince Louis, the eldest son of Saint-Louis (mid-XIIIth century); a capital decorated with hunting scenes (XVth century), etc. There is also a statue of the Virgin and Child in polychrome wood (early XIIIth century), fragments of stained-glass windows from churches in Paris (XVth and early XVIth centuries) and a scale model of Notre-Dame showing Viollet le Duc's restoration work.

THE VISITOR RETRACES

HIS STEPS ALONG THE

ARCADES SEPARATING

THE TWO PARTS OF THE

GARDEN

PARIS IN THE XVIth CENTURY AND UNDER HENRI IV

These rooms with their huge fireplaces, situated on the ground-floor of the main Renaissance building of the hôtel Carnavalet, evoke a XVIth century home.

No. 6 - *Retable* in Tonnerre stone, carved by Pierre Berton in 1542 for a chapel in the church of Saint-Merry. The architectural background was reconstituted from a contemporary document.

No. 7 - The Ligneris gallery. On show here and in the two adjoining rooms are the most ancient of the museum's views of Paris. Some of them were used as background for the most wide-ranging subjects: *l'Enfant prodigue chez les courtisanes*, for instance (Flemish school, mid-XVIth century), shows a musical gathering with "galant" overtones, set in a Parisian landscape; *Sainte-Geneviève gardant ses moutons* is an anonymous late XVIth century painting, showing a general view of Paris with the city's patron saint in the foreground. The urban landscape is sufficient in itself, however, in the *Vue du cimetière et de l'église des Saints-Innocents* (Flemish school, mid-XVIth century), which shows a very ancient group of buildings which disappeared at the end of the XVIIIth century. Also worth noting are an anonymous portrait of *François 1er*, "le roi chevalier et mécène", and the portrait of *Marie Stuart*, Queen of France and later Scotland, by (or after) the workshop of François Clouet.

No. 8 - The Catherine de Médicis gallery. Painted portraits of Queen *Catherine de Médicis*, the widow of Henri II, who ruled with a rod of iron during her Regency, and her second son *Charles IX*, both by (or after) the workshop of François Clouet. Two portraits attributed to François Quesnel: *Henri de Lorraine, Duc de Guise*, known as Le Balafré (Scarface), sworn enemy of all Protestants and head of the

**Pierre Berton. Part
of retable
in Tonnerre stone**

Ligue, and King *Henri III*, who was responsible for the
stabbing of the Duc de Guise at Blois in 1588. *La procession
de la Ligue dans l'île de la Cité*, a vast painting by an
unknown hand : this was probably based on the violent
demonstration organized in 1593 by the ultra-Catholic party,
who were opposed to the accession of Henri de Bourbon.
Despite this background of battles fought in the name of
religion, town planning construction in Paris made great
strides, as can be seen here in *Projet pour le Pont-Neuf*, an
anonymous painting inspired by a design which had received
the royal seal of approval; in 1578 Henri III laid the first
stone of what was a remarkably modern work for the time.

PARIS IN THE XVIth CENTURY AND UNDER HENRI IV

Catherine de Médicis

Anon.
Procession
de la Ligue
sur la place
de Grève

The Pont-Neuf was only completed in 1606, but its decoration was greatly simplified compared to the original.

No. 9 - The Henri IV gallery. *La procession de la Ligue sur la place de Grève*, an anonymous painting depicting another demonstration (in 1590 or 1593) by the ultra-Catholics. The procession, coming from the church of Saint-Jean en Grève, goes through an open archway under one of the buildings making up the Hôtel de Ville; the work which had begun there in 1533 seems to have been abandoned in mid-stream. An early XVIIth century anonymous painting,

PARIS IN THE XVIth CENTURY AND UNDER HENRI IV

Sainte Geneviève, patronne de Paris, devant l'Hôtel de Ville, shows the same building, now completed at the behest of Henri IV. A small picture, artist unknown, entitled *Henri IV à cheval devant Paris*, appears to commemorate the King's arrival in the city on 22nd March 1594. The palaces of the Louvre and the Tuileries, which were still not completed at the beginning of his reign, can be seen here quite clearly. *Scènes de la comédie italienne*, an anonymous painting from the end of the XVIth century, is certainly a portrayal of the Gelosi troupe, who were instrumental in the success of commedia dell'arte.

No. 10 - The Blue gallery. In the display cabinet on the wall is a small picture from the Dutch school dated 1606, a particularly harsh winter: *Patineurs sur la Seine devant le Louvre*. There are also four of the original masks from the Pont-Neuf, carved during the reign of Henri IV, and a collection of engravings from the XVIth century and the reign of Henri IV depicting buildings and achievements in town planning, Parisian events and portraits.

PARIS AND THE PARISIAN HOME UNDER LOUIS XIII AND LOUIS XIV

No. 11 - The Sévigné staircase, part of which dates from the XVIIth century. At the foot of the stairs, *Adelaïde de Savoie, duchesse de Bourgogne*, a terracotta replica of Antoine Coysevox' marble statue (Louvre museum), representing Louis XIVth's grand-daughter by marriage as Diana the huntress. Upstairs, *La Charité de Saint Martin*, a large painting by Georges Lallemant in the mannerism style, dating from approximately 1630, which originally belonged to the abbey church of Sainte-Geneviève.

No. 12 - The pictures in this little room and in the gallery next door mostly depict the growth and improvements in Paris under Louis XIII and before the coming-of-age of Louis XIV. A large anonymous painting represents the *Pont-Neuf* circa 1633 : a statue of Henri IV on horseback has been erected on the central reservation, and one can see the building containing the Samaritaine pump ; on the Right Bank, the remains of the Louvre of Philippe Auguste and Charles V, adjoining the parts of the palace built after the reign of François Ier. Small Louis XIII coffered ceiling with a mythological theme.

No. 13 - Three views of *La place Royale*, now the place des Vosges. This splendid example of architecture and town planning dates from the reign of Henri IV. It was completed during the regency of Marie de Médicis and inaugurated in 1612 with a grand tournament to mark Louis XIIIth's engagement. The theme of two of these anonymous paintings is the *Roman des chevaliers de la Gloire*. The third is a view of the square circa 1655, featuring the statue of Louis XIII on horseback which had been placed there in 1639.

The other pictures mainly depict the Seine and its

PARIS AND THE PARISIAN HOME
UNDER LOUIS XIII AND LOUIS XIV

banks. These were frequently painted by Flemish or Dutch artists, specialists of the urban scene. Four paintings by Abraham de Verwer, a highly perceptive Dutch artist, are of particular interest : the *Hôtel de Nevers* near the tour de Nesle, and the *Grande Galerie du Louvre* circa 1640, viewed in three different lights. The *quai de la Tournelle* circa 1646, a painting of the Dutch school attributed to Theodor Matham : a temporary wooden bridge leads to the île Notre-Dame, now the île de la Cité, where transformation and building work began in 1614. *La cité et l'île Notre-Dame* seen in firelight, artist unknown. *Marie de Médicis*, the Queen Regent, a painting from the school of François II Pourbus. Painted sketches for the religious compositions which hung at the time in the churches of Paris, i.e. the *Miracle de Saint-Paul* by

**View of
La place Royale, now
place des Vosges**

Francisque II Millet.
View of
L'Observatoire

Nicolas Loir, a sketch for the great "May" canvas belonging to Notre-Dame de Paris (1650).

No. 14 - On the ceiling is a large sketch by Bon Boullogne for an allegorical composition which served to decorate a ceiling in the Palais de Justice in 1688, *La Justice assure la Paix et protège les Arts*. Collection of XVIIth century engravings representing the most important buildings in Paris during the reigns of Louis XIII and Louis XIV.

No. 15 - The Paris of Louis XIV. The artists' recurrent theme remained the Seine and the view from or towards the Pont-Neuf. A number of anonymous views give an eye-witness account of the transformations which took place on this spot, particularly Louis le Vau's enlargement of the Louvre and the construction of the Collège

PARIS AND THE PARISIAN HOME
UNDER LOUIS XIII AND LOUIS XIV

des Quatre-Nations, now known as the Institut de France.

Two paintings are attributed to Francisque II Millet, one representing the *Observatoire*, which was erected in 1667 at the behest of Louis XIV, and the other the *Invalides*, founded by the King for the benefit of wounded soldiers, and built along the lines set out by Libéral Bruant between 1671 and 1676. Jules Hardouin-Mansart added a new church to it, the dome of which is now famous. This is the church which, as it nears completion, forms the main feature of Pierre-Denis Martin's painting, *Visite de Louis XIV à l'Hôtel royal des Invalides* on 26th August 1676. The same artist is responsible for *Paris vue du quai de Bercy* in 1716; one can pick out the île Notre-Dame or Saint-Louis, the Jardin des Plantes and the large Salpêtrière hospital, equally created under Louis XIV. A large anonymous painting shows the *Entrée d'Alvise*

**Drawing-room
of the Hôtel
Colbert de Villacerf**

Mocenigo, ambassadeur de la République de Venise, sur la place Royale on 20th January 1709.

In the glass display cabinet, illuminated manuscripts by Sevin, medals commemorating the buildings founded under Louis XIV.

No. 16 - The early XVIIIth century wood panelling comes from the former Pitié hospital in the rue Lacépède. A collection of gouaches from the Louis XIV period, depicting views of Paris, ballet costumes, scenes from popular everyday life.

No. 17 - Drawing-room of the hôtel Colbert de Villacerf. The Carnavalet museum owns a number of decorative ensembles from various buildings, which serve to illustrate the changes in style of the Parisian home from the XVIIth century on. This particular drawing-room, which can be dated approximately 1655, comes from a mansion in the Marais which has since been altered out of all recognition. It is a characteristic example of the style which was fashionable in Parisian town houses before Louis XIV came of age, with its gilt wood panelling, painted with "grotesque" polychromes, topped by a ceiling painted on canvas representing *Apollon et les Saisons*.

No. 18 - Painted sketches of pictures or mural compositions destined for churches in Paris during the reign of Louis XIV.

Nos. 19 and 20 - Main drawing-room and bedroom of the hôtel de la Rivière. This decorative ensemble comes from the apartments in the place Royale which Abbé de la Rivière had designed for his personal use by the architect François Le Vau, assisted by the painter Charles Le Brun.

PARIS AND THE PARISIAN HOME
UNDER LOUIS XIII AND LOUIS XIV

No. 19 - The large, richly-gilded drawing-room has retained some of its original wall decoration of fluted pilasters. The ceiling, upon which Le Brun painted *Le lever du jour*, is framed by wide arch coving, with stucco carvings of eagles, Cupids and garlands. Le Brun also conceived the two tapestries from the model entitled *Portières des Renommées*. A painting from the Beaubrun workshop shows la *Grande Mademoiselle* in the warrior rôle she played under la Fronde. *Décor pour l'opéra "Attys" de J.B. Lully*, artist unknown. Two paintings by René-Antoine Houasse, representing the *Transport de la statue équestre de Louis XIV* to place Louis le Grand (place Vendôme) in 1699. The creator of this bronze statue, which was destroyed during the Revolution, was François Girardon; only one foot, on show in this room, still remains of the royal effigy.

No. 20 - The main bedroom has only retained its original ceiling, painted on canvas, and the coving, painted on plaster. The decorative ensemble, by Charles Le Brun, depicts the *Histoire de Psyché*, with eight figures representing the Muses. Among the pictures exhibited in this room are four portraits of Louis XIII and Louis XIVth's contemporaries and views of two royal residences not far from Paris, painted around 1655 by Adam-Frans Van der Meulen, the Château de Vincennes and the *Château Neuf de Saint-Germain-en-Laye*.

No. 21 - The Sévigné gallery. The very plain panelling from the late XVIIth century has been preserved. It is in this room that Madame de Sévigné, who lived in the hôtel Carnavalet from 1677 until her death in 1696, is remembered. There are two portraits of *Madame de Sévigné*, one painted in oils some time between 1662 and 1665, by Claude Lefebvre, the other in pastel around 1670 by Robert

THE VISITOR SHOULD NOW RETRACE HIS STEPS AS FAR AS THE LANDING (No. 11)

René-Antoine Houasse.

Transport de la statue

équestre de Louis XIV

PARIS AND THE PARISIAN HOME
UNDER LOUIS XIII AND LOUIS XIV

Nanteuil. The first hangs above the japanned writing-flap desk used by the renowned letter-writer, which she brought from her home in Brittany, the château des Rochers. Portrait of Madame de Sévigné's daughter, *Madame de Grignan*, attributed to Pierre Mignard, and another of her husband the *Comte de Grignan*, painted by Nicolas de Largillière. There are also portraits of *Pierre Corneille* in later life, by François Sicre, *Molière*, attributed to Nicolas Mignard, and a pastel by Robert Nanteuil of *Guillaume de Lamoignon*, the president of the Paris Parliament.

No. 22 - A corner room which has retained its late XVIIth century wood panelling. The works shown here relate to the Regency period in Paris. A gouache by Pierre-Denis Martin depicts *Louis XV sortant du lit de Justice tenu le 12 septembre 1715*; in the presence of the young King, whose magnificent retinue can be seen crossing the cour de Mai, in front of the Sainte-Chapelle, the Regent had convened Parliament in the Palais de Justice in order to reverse Louis XIVth's will. Another painting by the same artist shows the *Cortège de Mehemet Effendi, ambassadeur de l'empire ottoman, sortant de l'audience accordée par le roi* on 21st March 1721, crossing the Pont-Royal bridge.

No. 23 - Collection of china from the XVIIth and early XVIIIth centuries, from Nevers, Rouen, Delft, etc...

THE VISITOR SHOULD NOW RETRACE HIS STEPS AS FAR AS THE LANDING (No. 11)

THE PARIS MUNICIPALITY UNDER THE ANCIEN REGIME

These three rooms stand where Madame de Sévigné's main apartments used to be. There are portraits of members of the Bureau de la Ville de Paris, which before the Revolution was composed of the merchants' provost, four elected municipal magistrates, a clerk of the court, the receiver and the public prosecutor. Since the reign of Henri IV, these municipal officers had been regularly portrayed in vast compositions aimed at recording their time in office for future generations. These enormous paintings were hung in the Hôtel de Ville. The ones seen here escaped the

Claude Lefebvre.
Madame de Sévigné

THE PARIS MUNICIPALITY UNDER THE 'ANCIEN REGIME

Revolution. They are shown alongside sketches painted for other works in the same series and individual portraits of some of the merchants' provosts or municipal magistrates.

No. 24 - The fireplace with its carved and painted panelling dates from approximately 1630 and comes from a mansion in the rue des Bernardins. This room features two large pictures from the Hôtel de Ville, one dated 1611, by Georges Lallemant, and the other 1614, artist unknown, as well as a portrait taken from a large painting by Philippe de Champaigne, dated 1654. Sketch by Noël Coypel for a large painting commissioned in 1674, *le Corps de Ville allant rendre grâces à Notre-Dame après la victoire de Senef.*

No. 25 - Two fragments of a large painting by Nicolas de Largillière commissioned in 1702 by the Ville de Paris to commemorate the duc d'Anjou's accession to the

Noël Coypel.
Le corps de ville
allant rendre grâces
à Notre-Dame après
la victoire de Séneffe

Spanish throne: *Le prévôt des marchands Boucher d'Orsay* and *Deux Echevins*. Sketches by the same painter and by Carle Van Loo.

No. 26 - *Publication de la paix d'Aix la Chapelle*, a painting by Jacques Dumont, also known as le Romain. This vast composition was commissioned by the Ville de Paris in 1758 and features portraits of municipal officers in a richly allegorical representation. Painted sketches for pictures commissioned by the Hôtel de Ville between 1763 and 1782, by Jean-Baptiste Deshayes, Noël Hallé, Joseph-Marie Vien et François-Guillaume Ménageot. A portrait painted in 1771 by Joseph-Silfrède Duplessis of *François de La Michodière*, later to become merchants' provost. *La Ville de Paris*, Etienne Bourchardon's original plaster model of the famous rue de Grenelle fountain (1739-1745). In the display cabinet, objects bearing the arms of the Ville de Paris: bindings, medals, pottery, purses, the sword of a night watchman.

PARIS UNDER LOUIS XV

The paintings which hang in these two galleries show the face of Paris between approximately 1720 and 1760, during which period houses built for private use flourished (the mansions in the faubourgs Saint-Honoré and Saint-Germain, for instance), making up for the relative stagnation on the town planning and architectural fronts.

No. 27 - Nine views of Paris and its environs, painted around 1740 by Charles-Léopold de Grevenbrœck, a specialist in urban landscapes with an invaluable eye for detail : *Vue générale prise du haut de Belleville, Vue des Champs-Elysées depuis les hauteurs de Chaillot, Vue de la Seine devant les hauteurs de Chaillot et de Passy, etc.*

No. 28 - The carved and painted panelling in this room, which comes from a mansion in the rue de Varenne, is a fine example of the "rocaille" style. The ceiling, attributed to Jean-Jacques Lagrenée, painted on canvas, represents the *Triomphe de Flore*; it comes from the "folly" (country house) of a certain M. Vassal in the rue Blanche.

Charles-Laurent de Grevenbrœck. Vue des Champs- Elysées depuis les hauteurs de Chaillot

THE VISITOR SHOULD LEAVE THIS GALLERY BY THE WOODEN STAIRCASE AND RETURN ONCE MORE THROUGH THE PORCH SEPARATING THE TWO PARTS OF THE GARDEN

No. 29 - This gallery is almost entirely devoted to the work of Nicolas Jean-Baptiste Raguenet. In these views of Paris, painted in the mid-XVIIIth century, this fairly minor artist's scrupulously accurate observation provides an invaluable record of contemporary Paris, tempered with a hint of poetry.

The Seine links all these urban landscapes together. Several views are worth noting, depicting the Cité, Notre-Dame, the Archevêché, the canons' houses; the Pont-Neuf, showing the Samaritaine pump, built under Henri IV and rebuilt during the reign of Louis XIV, which supplied water from the river to the surrounding areas; the île Saint-Louis, with its bridges and fine houses; the Hôtel de Ville, Louvre, Tuileries, Chaillot and Passy.

Perhaps the most picturesque view is of the *Pont Notre-Dame*, with its depiction of the bargemen's water jousting tournament beneath the arches, which still supported two rows of houses at the time.

Nicolas Jean-Baptiste Raguenet. View of the Pont Notre-Dame

THE DECORATIVE ENSEMBLES OF CLAUDE-NICOLAS LEDOUX

By the end of Louis XVth's reign, the great architect Ledoux was already contributing to the triumph of the neo-classical style. His inventive originality appeared not only in his buildings, of which there were many examples in Paris, but also in his work as interior decorator, as can be seen in the two reconstitutions shown here.

No. 30 - The Café militaire. The decoration dates from 1762. Situated in the rue Saint-Honoré, this café was the meeting-place for the King's armies, which explains why the ornamental items, carved in the antique mode, are so martially-oriented. On one of the walls hangs a painting attributed to Callet, *Claude-Nicolas Ledoux et sa fille*.

No. 31 - Reception-room of the hôtel d'Uzès. This mansion, which had been built by Ledoux himself in the rue Montmartre, was demolished in the XIXth century. The white and gold panelling was carved in 1767 by Joseph Métivier and Jean-Baptiste Boiston under the architect's instructions. The doors are decorated with symbols of the four corners of the universe. The design of the large wall panels is particularly original, depicting treetrunks hung with musical instruments and other appendages.

The furniture is Louis XVI. Terracotta bust of the composer *Gluck*, by François Martin.

**Reception-room of
the Hôtel d'Uzès**

THE PARISIAN HOME AND LIFE IN PARIS UNDER LOUIS XV UNTIL APPROXIMATELY 1760

No. 32 - The Luynes.staircase. This staircase was built at the beginning of the XXth century. It frames the vast murals which used to adorn the staircase of the hôtel de Luynes in the faubourg Saint-Germain. These were the work of Paolo Antonio Brunetti, an Italian painter renowned for his interior decorations, and they make use of trompe-l'œil architecture to show off an elegant gathering sampling the delights of love, music and flowers.

A fine collection of furniture and works of art (donated for the most part by Madame Henriette Bouvier in 1965), in a setting of wood-panelled walls from former Parisian mansions, illustrate the art of the Parisian home.

HAVING CLIMBED THIS STAIRCASE TO THE FIRST FLOOR, THE VISITOR FINDS HIMSELF IN A SERIES OF ROOMS, THE FIRST OF WHICH OPENS DIRECTLY ON TO THE LANDING.

No. 33 - The Bouvier room. This room and the two adjoining ones (nos. 34 and 35) house furniture and objects from the period of Louis XIV (small table in carved oak, candlesticks on pedestal tables, a pair of small inlaid cupboards in Boulle style, bronze statuettes), the Regency period (three wardrobes, bookcases, a pair of corner cupboards) and the reign of Louis XV (chest of drawers showing the hallmark of the cabinet maker Charles Migeon).

No. 36 - The Gilt room. Blue and gold coffered ceiling, circa 1650, from the hôtel Bouthillier de Chavigny (7-9, rue de Sévigné). *Faune au chevreau*, a bronze model by the Florentine sculptor Massimiliano Soldani (1658-1740).

No. 37 - The Louis XV blue room. Regency panelling from the hôtel de Broglie in the faubourg Saint-Germain. Two writing-flap desks by the cabinet maker Adrien Delorme. "Duchesse brisée" style chaise longue in two sections by the carpenter Sylvain Blanchard.

No. 38 - The Louis XV grey room. Regency panelling from the hôtel de l'Aubespine (formerly on the quai

Luynes staircase

**Regency corner
cupboard.
Bouvier room**

THE PARISIAN HOME AND LIFE IN PARIS
UNDER LOUIS XV UNTIL APPROXIMATELY 1760

Malaquais). Writing-flap desk by François Reizell, small
sewing-table by Adrien Delorme.

No. 39 - Polychrome room. The Louis XV
panelling, from a mansion in the rue de Fleurus, has retained
its original paintwork. *Etude de pied pour le portrait de
Mademoiselle O'Murphy*, pastel by François Boucher. In the
display cabinets : china, porcelain, fans, wax figurines from
the XVIIIth century.

No. 40 - Small salon. Panelling from the
transitional period between the two kings, Louis XV and
Louis XVI, from a mansion in the faubourg Saint-Germain.
High-sided Louis XV couch.

No. 41 - Louis XV panelling from various sources.
Portrait of the engraver *Jean Mariette*, painted by Antoine
Pesne. Paintings depicting life in Paris under Louis XV : *la
Partie de billard*, one of Jean-Baptiste Chardin's early works ;
le Carnaval des rues de Paris and *le Transport des filles de joie
à la Salpêtrière*, by Etienne Jeaurat.

No. 42 - Polychrome decorated panels with Chinese
motifs, origin unknown (mid-XVIIIth century).

THE VISITOR SHOULD START WITH THE ROOM ON HIS RIGHT.

THE VISITOR RETRACES HIS STEPS AS FAR AS THE SMALL SALON (No. 40), THEN ENTERS THE ROOM OPPOSITE HIM

Louis XV blue room,
with panelling from
the Hôtel de Broglie,
rue Saint-Dominique.
Regency

Massimiliano Soldani.
Faune au chevreau

THE PARISIAN HOME AND LIFE IN PARIS
UNDER LOUIS XV UNTIL APPROXIMATELY 1760

No. 43 - The Louis XV turquoise room. The panelling, circa 1740, is in the "rocaille" style, and comes from the hôtel Brulart de Genlis (13, quai Conti). Magnificent red lake chest of drawers with gilt decorations and writing-flap desk with polychrome motifs on a bright yellow background, by unknown cabinet makers.

Rosewood desk with writing-flap bearing the Delorme hallmark. Louis XV

No. 44 - The Louis XV saffron room. Richly carved panelling in the "rocaille" style, circa 1735, from the mansion known as l'hôtel des Stuart d'Aubigny (located in the rue Gay-Lussac). Two japanned chests of drawers with gilt decorations, made by the cabinet maker Jacques Dubois.

No. 45 - A few paintings depicting religious life in Paris during the first half of the XVIIIth century: *Cardinal de Noailles, Archevêque de Paris*, anon; sketches for large Parisian church paintings, by Carle Van Loo, Gabriel Doyen, Noël Hallé. Painted banner from the brotherhood of Saint Sépulcre, from the church of the same name.

No. 46 - The Prémontrés chamber. The Louis XV panelling comes from the former Prémontrés convent, which was situated in the rue Hautefeuille. Two early XVIIIth century chests of drawers. Carved oak console in "rocaille" style. Two terracotta models of statues for the church of Saint Sulpice by François Dumont.

No. 47 - The Louis XV panelling comes from the hôtel Brulart de Genlis. This room is devoted to the theatre under Louis XV. A suite of four figures in polychrome wood are of particular interest; they come from the Seraphin theatre at the Palais-Royal and represent characters from the Italian theatre.

No. 48 - Panelling of unknown origin. This room illustrates the vital rôle of writers, philosophers, encyclopaedists and other great minds in French XVIIIth century society. The fame and obvious influence of Voltaire and Rousseau are clearly shown in the large collection of memorabilia connected with them. *Voltaire dans sa jeunesse*, an XVIIIth century portrait painted after Nicolas de Largillière. An amusing little picture by the Swiss painter

THE PARISIAN HOME AND LIFE IN PARIS
UNDER LOUIS XV UNTIL APPROXIMATELY 1760

**Anon. Bust of
Voltaire. Terracotta**

Jean Hubert, *Lever de Voltaire à Ferney*, marble statuette by
Jean-Baptiste Rosset. A pair of terracotta busts of *Voltaire*
and *Rousseau*, artist unknown. Also in this room, a painting
by Jacques de Lajoue of the physician *L'Abbé Nollet* in his
study at la Muette, a portrait of the philosopher and
mathematician *Jean de Rond d'Alembert* by Catherine Lusurier
and a portrait by Jean-Simon Berthélémy of *Diderot*,
who won worldwide acclaim with his "Encyclopédie".

THE VISITOR CROSSES
THE LANDING OF THE
"ESCALIER DE LUYNES"
(No. 32) AND ENTERS
THE SERIES OF ROOMS
OPPOSITE

PARIS AND THE PARISIAN HOME AT THE END OF LOUIS XVth's REIGN AND UNDER LOUIS XVI

These rooms cover a very brief period - barely thirty years - but one which was crucially important in the history of Paris. It was at this time, as the Ancien Régime gradually gave way to the Revolution, that the neo-classical style first appeared; it went on to flourish not only in architecture and town planning, as these paintings and models show, but also within the home, as can be seen from the interior decoration, furniture and works of art here, donated for the most part by Madame Henriette Bouvier, like the objects from the previous period, displayed alongside portraits and historical souvenirs.

Nos. 49 and 50 - Corridor. Large portrait of *Louis XVI en costume de sacre* by Joseph-Silfrède Duplessis.

Nos. 51 to 55 - Panelling from the hôtel de Breteuil, which used to stand in the rue Matignon.

No. 51 - Round boudoir.

No. 52 - The Louis XVI yellow room. Among other items of furniture, a beautiful chest of drawers bearing the double hallmark of the cabinet makers Weisweiller and Riesener.

No. 53 - The Louis XVI blue room. Among other works, two genre paintings by Michel Garnier, valuable for their portrayal of costume: the *Contrat de Mariage Interrompu* and its counterpart the *Départ du Volontaire*.

No. 54 - Corridor.

No. 55 - Oval boudoir. Elegant desk cabinet by Jean-Honoré Riesener.

Nos. 56 and 57 - Pictures and models commemorating the main achievements in town planning and architecture at the end of Louis XVth's reign. *Cérémonie de la pose de la première pierre de la nouvelle église Sainte-Geneviève* on 6th September 1764, by Pierre-Antoine de Machy. The

PARIS AND THE PARISIAN HOME AT THE END
OF LOUIS XVth's REIGN AND UNDER LOUIS XVI

architect Soufflot shows the King the plans for what is now the
Pantheon. The church façade is actually a trompe-l'œil model
painted specially for the occasion. Other paintings by de
Machy depict the clearing of the Louvre colonnade. *Chapelle
du Calvaire dans l'Eglise St-Roch*, by Nicolas-Bernard
Lépicié, a curious group of buildings designed by the
architect Boullée and the sculptor Falconet. A portrait of
Edme Bouchardon by François-Hubert Drouais. The sculptor
is shown standing in front of a wax model of his most famous
work, the bronze statue of Louis XV on horseback, which was
inaugurated in the place Louis XV in 1763 and destroyed in
1792. A fragment of the statue, the King's hand, is placed
near the portrait. The place Louis XV, now place de la
Concorde, was especially designed by the architect Gabriel to
show the statue to advantage; three anonymous paintings show
it as it was before the transformations, at one stage during the
work and once completed. *L'école royale de chirurgie en
construction*, a painting by Hubert Robert; this important neo-
classical building, now the Faculté de Médecine, was
completed in 1769 by the architect Jacques Gondouin, whose
portrait in pastel by Louis Valade can also be seen here. Two
models of architecture from the same period: the *façade de
l'église de la Madeleine*, as depicted by Pierre Contant d'Ivry
in a project which was never adopted, and the *façade de
Saint-Sulpice*, the work of Servandoni, showing Jean-François
Chalgrin's design for the North tower (later implemented).

No. 58 - The Demarteau room. François Boucher
was commissioned around 1765 by his friend, the engraver
Demarteau, to produce this ensemble of paintings on canvas,
set into wooden panelling, which Demarteau used to decorate
his shop situated in the Cité area, rue de la Pelleterie. It is

made to look like a trellised house overlooking a garden. Boucher himself probably did the tint drawings of Cupids painted on three of the doors, but he was assisted by Honoré Fragonard, who composed the more lyrical Cupid on the fourth door, and animal painters such as Jean-Baptiste Huet.

No. 60 - Passage. Paintings by Pierre-Antoine de Machy : *Intérieur de l'église de la Madeleine*, based on the design by Contant d'Ivry (see No. 57), *Intérieur et extérieur de l'église des Saints-Innocents* during its demolition, *Vente publique de tableaux*. Louis XVI wardrobe containing china decorated with air balloons, which were invented in 1783.

No. 61 - The Louis XVI panelling in this and the three adjoining rooms comes from the château de Conflans in

Chest with three drawers, mahogany veneer, bearing the hallmark of Riesener and Weisweiller. Louis XVI

PARIS AND THE PARISIAN HOME AT THE END OF LOUIS XVth's REIGN AND UNDER LOUIS XVI

Charenton, just outside Paris, the "extra muros" residence of the archbishops of Paris. The plaster bust of the architect and engineer *Perronet*, by François Masson, stands next to two models created in his workshop - the Pont Louis XVI, now the Pont de la Concorde, and a decorative detail. A picture by Hubert Robert shows another example of his art, le *Décintrement du Pont de Neuilly*, a technical achievement carried out in 1772. *L'Incendie de l'Opéra* in 1781 is by the same artist; the theatre was at that time at the Palais-Royal. Attractive terracotta bust of *Dorothée Luzy*, a member of the Comédie Française, by Jean-Jacques Caffieri (1776).

No. 62 - Works by Pierre-Antoine de Machy: paintings showing the *Foire Saint-Germain* during and after the 1762 fire; gouache depicting the construction of the *Halle au Blé*, a building in the neo-classical style designed by Le Grand and Molinos.

No. 63 - Paintings showing the demolition of houses on the *Pont Notre-Dame* (1786) and the *Pont au Change* (1788), by Hubert Robert.

Hubert Robert. Demolition of houses on the Pont Notre-Dame

THE FURNITURE
DONATED BY MADAME
DEBRAY IS ON SHOW IN
THIS ROOM FOR THE
MOMENT, BUT WILL BE
MOVING TO ROOM No. 68
AS SOON AS IT IS
READY

No. 64 - An anonymous painting depicts the *Hôtel de Salm en construction*; designed by the architect Rousseau, this neo-classical building is now the Palais de la Légion d'Honneur. *Le Duc de Chartres recevant les clefs de la Folie Monceau*, attributed to Louis Carrogis, otherwise known as Carmontelle, shows one of the first gardens "à l'anglaise" created in France; it is now the Parc Monceau. Several views of Paris by Jean-Baptiste Lallemand, Jean-Baptiste Genillion and Alexandre Noël. A large picture by Philibert Louis Debucourt shows the *Fête populaire aux Halles* which took place on 21st January 1782 in honour of the Dauphin's birth.

No. 65 - This is where the smaller temporary exhibitions will be held.

THE TOUR CONTINUES
ON THE SECOND FLOOR.
ROOMS 65 TO 68 WILL
ONLY BE OPENED TO
THE PUBLIC AT THE END
OF 1990

No. 66 - *Les Galeries du Palais-Royal*. Executed around 1845 by Regnard, this large scale model faithfully reproduces the three long main buildings created between 1781 and 1785 by the architect Victor Louis around the Palais-Royal gardens, at the request of the duc de Chartres, as well as the many shops which

PARIS AND THE PARISIAN HOME AT THE END
OF LOUIS XVth's REIGN AND UNDER LOUIS XVI

existed under the arcades at the time of the July Monarchy.

No. 67 - Passage. Four bas-reliefs by Nicolas Sébastien Adam, *Scènes du mythe d'Apollon*, from the house in the rue de Clichy built around 1760 for the farmer-general La Bouexière.

No. 68 - The Louis XVI panelling, as in rooms 61 to 64, comes from the château de Conflans, the residence of the archbishops of Paris. The Louis XVI furniture (donated by Madame Nelly Debray) includes three chests of drawers bearing the hallmarks of Nicolas Petit, R.V.L.C. (Roger Vandercruse, otherwise known as Lacroix) and J.H. Riesener, as well as a backgammon table made by the latter.

BEYOND THIS POINT ARE THE CULTURAL AND TEACHING WORKSHOPS (NOT INCLUDED IN THE GENERAL TOUR OF THE MUSEUM; DETAILS OF THE ACTIVITIES ON REQUEST).

THE VISITOR GOES BACK DOWN TO THE GROUND-FLOOR, CROSSES THE GARDEN AND ROOMS 30 AND 31, AND ARRIVES AT THE FOOT OF THE "ESCALIER DE LUYNES". FROM THERE, HE CAN EITHER VISIT THE TEMPORARY EXHIBITION ROOMS OR RETURN TO THE RECEPTION AREA, WHERE HE WILL FIND THE EXIT AND ALSO ACCESS TO THE HÔTEL LE PELETIER DE SAINT-FARGEAU (SEE BELOW).

Nos. 69 to 80 - The main temporary exhibitions organized by the museum will be held in this series of rooms. The rooms are closed to the public when no exhibition is being held.

Historical background of the hôtel Le Peletier de St-Fargeau

This mansion was built around 1690 for Michel Le Peletier, seigneur de Souzy, State councillor and financial administrator. The plans were drawn up by Pierre Bullet, who designed the porte Saint-Martin and a great many private residences in Paris. Its architectural style is sober, verging on the severe, as befits a magistrate's home. No decorative carvings adorn the main courtyard or the façade overlooking the rue de Sévigné. The West-oriented façade, which used to give on to the garden of the house, now the square Georges-Cain, and the façade of the orangery, erected by Bullet at right angles facing North, are rather more generous with their carvings. The main staircase and a gilt-panelled room on the first floor are the only original items of interior decoration.

HISTORIQUE

The house was once occupied by its founder's great-grandson, Michel Etienne Le Peletier, seigneur de Saint-Fargeau, President of the Parliament, deputy for the nobility before the 1789 States General, then member of the Convention. On 20th January 1793, he voted in favour of the King's immediate execution, but was assassinated that very evening in a café near the Palais Royal by the former bodyguard Pâris, who wished in this way to prove his loyalty to the King.

The daughter of the regicide member of the Convention sold the house in 1811, and it was then used for a variety of purposes. The Ville de Paris bought it in 1898 to contain its historical library, and the premises had to be expanded by a group of buildings, stretching Northwards right up to the square Léopold-Achille.

By a strange coincidence, the home of the regicide "martyr of the Revolution", as he came to be known after his assassination, now houses the revolutionary collections of the Carnavalet museum.

The converted gallery on the first floor of the building housing the lycée Victor Hugo links the two parts of the museum and can be reached either from the reception area situated on the ground-floor of the hôtel Carnavalet or from room 45, on the first floor.

The far end of the gallery comes out on the first floor of the hôtel Le Peletier de Saint-Fargeau, at the foot of staircase . The main courtyard of the house, which is not open to visitors, can be seen from the windows. Pierre Bullet's somewhat severe architectural style is revealed in all its dignity. The purity of outline compensates for the lack of any carved decoration. It should be remembered that the building facing the street, as one enters through the porch, has been enlarged, and had an extra floor added to it at a very late stage.

THE VISITOR SHOULD GO STRAIGHT UP TO THE SECOND FLOOR

Engraving of Louis Michel Le Peletier de Saint-Fargeau. Not on show

Paris
from 1789 to
the present day

Although the Carnavalet museum is not strictly speaking the museum of the French Revolution, in that it covers the entire history of Paris, it certainly owns the world's most important collection devoted to this brief (1789-1799) but crucial period, whose far-reaching events shattered the whole structure of French society and its institutions. As the Revolution was mainly played out in Paris, this seemed the obvious place for the collection to be housed. Paintings and sculptures by famous artists, such as Hubert Robert or Joseph Chinard, or lesser-known names like Charles Thévenin, Jean-Baptiste Lallemand and Joseph Doncre, not to mention those who remain anonymous to this day, rub shoulders with the rather naïve suite of gouaches by Le Sueur and a complementary iconographical source supplied by contemporary prints. There are also a great number of objects from civil and military life (furniture, clocks, china and porcelain, containers and snuff-boxes, insignia, arms, drums, flags, etc.) decorated in the spirit of the Revolution, and last but not least objects which may have little intrinsic artistic interest, but which do shed valuable light on the people and events of the time.

THE FRENCH REVOLUTION

The policy of the Carnavalet museum is to display works of art and other items which are contemporary with the events and people they represent or evoke. Their period is therefore not specified here.

No. 100 - On the top landing, two large anonymous canvases, in the naïf style, convey in allegorical fashion the hopes raised in 1789 by the convening of the States General and the King's goodwill.

No. 101 - The States General. Two more anonymous canvases make up a suite of four. In one of the large display cabinets, prints and various other items relating to the financial crisis at the end of the Ancien Régime, the assembly of "Notables", the first troubles, the convening and progress of the States General, the creation of the National Assembly, etc. Terracotta by Fickaert, *Projet de monument à la gloire de Necker*, Louis XVIth's popular Minister of Finance. Painting attributed to Callet, *Portrait de Louis XVI*. *Le serment du Jeu de Paume*, a painting attributed to Louis David, which may have been the sketch for his great unfinished work : on 20th June 1789 the deputies from the National Assembly, led by Bailly, met at Versailles in an indoor tennis court, and swore to give the kingdom a constitution ; this was the birth of the Constituent Assembly. Iconography of the main protagonists : bust of *Jean-Sylvain Bailly*, the astronomer and president of the Constituent Assembly, by Louis Pierre Deseine ; bust of *Honoré Riquetti, comte de Mirabeau*, by Tessier, a little-known sculptor, who managed to capture the powerful personality of the famous orator ; anonymous *portrait de Mirabeau*. In the second display cabinet, collection of china from Nevers, Roanne, Varzy and manufacturing industries in Northern and Eastern France,

**Hubert Robert.
La Bastille au début
de sa démolition**

**China from the
revolutionary period**

THE FRENCH REVOLUTION

with polychrome decoration inspired by the affection which the people still felt in 1789 for their King, but also depicting the hopes raised by the States General; the emphasis is laid alternately on the claims of the Third Estate and the union of the three orders.

No. 102 - The Bastille. This room is devoted not only to the famous events of 14th July 1789 but also to the incidents immediately preceding and following that fateful day. On the right as one enters the room is a portrait of *Jean-Henri Masers, dit le chevalier de Latude,* by Antoine Vestier, recalling Masers' successful escape from the Bastille in 1764, where he had been imprisoned for organizing a mock attempt on the life of Madame de Pompadour; the ropeladder used for the escape is on show next to the portrait. Bust of *Camille Desmoulins* by François Martin. This well-known journalist and public speaker played a vital rôle in the July 1789 uprising. Two paintings by Jean-Baptiste Lallemand: *Charge du prince de Lambesc au jardin des Tuileries* on 12th July (a demonstration by the crowd, revolting against Necker's dismissal, was violently quashed); *Pillage des armes aux Invalides,* on the morning of 14th July. *La prise de la Bastille:* this erstwhile fortress, which had become the most infamous of the royal prisons, symbolised arbitrary punishment, using orders issued under the King's private seal to imprison people without trial. It had only seven prisoners left when it was attacked by rioters searching for arms. Following a bloody battle, the prison governor de Launay was murdered. The symbolic effect of this event led to its portrayal in several pictures, notably a painting attributed to Jean-Baptiste Lallemand, an allegorical interpretation by Charles Thévenin and a large painting in the naïf style by an unknown artist. *La*

Bastille au début de sa démolition, painted by Hubert Robert; work began on this immediately after the storming of the Bastille, and was completed by the end of the year. The contractor in charge of the demolition, Palloy, hit on the idea of making commercial or advertising profit from "souvenirs" made with stones from the building, for instance a series of models of the Bastille; one of them is on show here. *M. de Flesselles, le dernier prévôt des marchands, massacré sur le perron de l'Hôtel de Ville*, painted by Jean-Baptiste Lallemand; this assassination took place on 14th July, just after the storming of the Bastille. In the display cabinet, small pictures, prints and sundry objects relating to the storming and demolition of the Bastille; prints giving an iconographical account of the abolition of privileges (night of 4th August 1789) and the royal family's return to Paris (October 1789).

Charles Thévenin. La Fête de la Fédération

THE FRENCH REVOLUTION

No. 103 - Federation Day. This grand celebration of national reconciliation took place on the first anniversary of the storming of the Bastille, on 14th July 1790. As one comes into the room, two anonymous paintings can be seen reproducing in an allegorical context the famous *Déclaration des Droits de l'Homme et du Citoyen*, voted as early as 26th August 1789. The celebration itself is covered in three large paintings : the first in the naïf style, artist unknown ; the second by Pierre-Antoine de Machy and his workshop ; and last but by no means least, Charles Thévenin's minutely observed work, in which one can recognize the main protagonists, from Louis XVI to Robespierre. A curious anonymous painting entitled *Serment de La Fayette* shows the hero of the American War of Independence, who enjoyed tremendous popularity at the time, before the altar to the homeland ; on the extreme right of the picture one can see Talleyrand, then Bishop of Autun. In the display cabinet are prints and sundry objects connected with Federation Day, which is richly supplied with iconographical material, and with various other contemporary events belonging to this relatively peaceful period in the history of the French Revolution.

No. 104 - From the monarchy to the republic. This room covers the brief period of constitutional monarchy, under Legislative Assembly rule, from the end of 1790 to the end of 1792, and the abolition of royalty caused by the events of 10th August 1792, the September massacres and the setting-up of a Republican régime. In the display cabinet : allegorical terracotta sculptures by Joseph Chinard ; Etienne Gois' plaster model of his *Monument à Voltaire*, whose ashes were transferred to the Pantheon on 11th July 1791 ; prints relating

Joseph Chinard. Jupiter foudroyant l'aristocratie. Allegorical sculpture. Plaster

the flight to Varenne (20th to 25th June 1791), the firing at
the Champ de Mars (17th July 1791), the events of 10th
August, the September massacres. Against the walls, plaster
bust of *Louis XVI*, the constitutional monarch, by Louis-Pierre
Deseine (1791); two large cupboards, which used to be in the
Convention room, covered in wallpaper printed with the 1793
revised version of the *Table des Droits de l'Homme et du
Citoyen* and the 1793 *Table de l'Acte Constitutionnel*, which
never really came into force. Inlaid dresser in two sections,
decorated with revolutionary emblems and drawings. Plaster
bust of *Barnave*, a model by Antoine Houdon; this great
Republican orator was executed in 1793, falling victim to his
own moderation, like so many of the famous Girondin
deputies in the Convention, as conveyed by Laurent
Blanchard's curious *Hommage aux Girondins*.

     No. 105 - The royal family. On 10th August 1792,
Louis XVI found himself suspended by the Legislative
Assembly and was arrested and imprisoned in the Temple
dungeon along with Marie-Antoinette, their children Madame
Royale (later Duchesse d'Angoulême) and the Dauphin Louis
XVII, and his sister Madame Elisabeth. The Convention tried
the King on 3rd December; he was sentenced to death on
18th January 1793 and decapitated three days later.
Malesherbes, the King's counsel for the defence, is depicted
here in a pastel by Louis Valade. Moving portrait of *Louis XVI*
by Joseph Ducreux, probably the last drawing ever made of
him. Painting by the Marquise de Bréhan of *Marie-Antoinette
à la prison de la Conciergerie*. A pair of paintings by Jean-
Jacques Hauer, *Adieux de Louis XVI à sa famille* and *Louis
XVI enlevé aux siens*. Two Danish pictures in the naïf style,
Exécution de Louis XVI sur la place de la Révolution and

THE FRENCH REVOLUTION

Exécution de Marie-Antoinette, which took place on the same spot, on 16th October 1793. A portrait of *Louis XVII* painted in the Temple in 1793 by Vien le fils. In the display cabinet a number of items relating to the royal family, and in particular their imprisonment (writing exercise by the Dauphin, laundry list, geometry set belonging to Louis XVI).

No. 106 - The Temple. This room is viewed from the doorway. Although this is not an exact replica of the prison located in the former Temple priory, the royal family's time in captivity is tellingly conveyed by the modest items of furniture which were made available to them: the King's bookcase, the Queen's dressing-table and bottles of perfume, Madame Elisabeth's bed.

No. 107 - The Convention and the Terror. In this passage and in room 108, the most dramatic period of the Revolution - late 1792 to July 1794 - is evoked. At the National Convention, i.e. the Republican Assembly, moderate "Girondin" deputies found themselves up against the "Montagnards", whose triumph was secured at the price of bloodshed. The Committee for Public Safety, under Robespierre's ruthless dictatorship, became to all intents and purposes the government. The excesses of the Terror were blamed on the war declared against Europe. Despite a number of impressive ceremonies, however, there was no glossing over the judgments without trial, massacres and famine. Anonymous portraits in pastels of the Girondins *Léon Buzot* and *Jérôme Pétion*, mayor of Paris. Three small pictures by Hubert Robert showing the prison of Saint-Lazare, where the painter was incarcerated during the Terror: the milk distribution, a corridor, a ball game in the courtyard. In the display cabinet, a collection of popular china from the

Republican era, decorated with emblems and revolutionary allegories.

      No. 108 - The Convention, the Terror (contd.). In the middle of the room stands a china stove presented to the Convention by Ollivier, a potter in the faubourg Saint-Antoine; it is a reproduction of the Bastille in relief. On the walls, portraits of the leading "Montagnards" and major contributors to the dramatic events of the time : *Camille Desmoulins*, anon. ; the famous orator was accused of indulgence and died a victim of Robespierre, like his young wife, *Lucile*, painting attributed to Louis-Léopold Boilly and

Joseph Ducreux.
Portrait of Louis XVI
a few days before
his execution.
Black chalk drawing

Anon.

Georges Danton

the fiery *Georges Danton*, anon. ; *Jean-Paul Marat*, painted by
Joseph Boze, who has astutely captured the tormented look of
the popular speaker and outspoken editor of "L'Ami du
Peuple", stabbed in his bath on 13th July 1793 by *Charlotte
Corday*, as depicted in a small anonymous picture, and
mourned in great pomp at the former church of Les Cordeliers

- see *Pompe funèbre de Marat* (the David school of painting).
A striking portrait of *Maximilien de Robespierre* by an
unknown artist, showing the "Incorruptible"'s stony glare and
outward appearance of the well-groomed, stilted bourgeois; a
bust by Giuseppe Ceracchi, *Barère de Vieuzac*. Three
paintings by Pierre-Antoine de Machy and his workshop show
on the one hand an *Exécution capitale*, place de la
Révolution, now place de la Concorde, where the guillotine
stood from 10th May 1793 until 13th June 1794, and on the
other, two important revolutionary celebrations, the *Fête de
l'Unité*, which took place on that same spot on 10th August
1793, the first anniversary of the Republic, and the *Fête de
l'Être Suprême*, which occurred on 8th June 1794 in the
Champ de Mars, at the instigation of Robespierre, who
wanted to introduce a new form of deist worship, inspired by
the ideas of Jean-Jacques Rousseau. Wheelchair used by
Couthon, a member of the Committee for Public Safety, who
was paralysed. In the large display cabinet: a pair of
anonymous polychrome busts of *Le Peletier de Saint-Fargeau*
and *Marat*, an example of the iconographical celebration
which associated the two "martyrs of the Revolution", the first
of whom was assassinated on the eve of Louis XVIth's
execution because he had voted in favour of the death
sentence. Souvenirs of Danton (cutlery kit, silver spoon and
fork), Robespierre (wallet, shaving-dish), Saint-Just (pistol),
small-scale models of the guillotine. Small portrait by Jean-
François Garneray of the Paris Opera singer *Mademoiselle
Maillard*, who incarnated the goddess Reason in the atheist
celebration of 10th November 1793, in a deconsecrated
Notre-Dame de Paris. Prints relating the main events during
the Terror. Small allegorical sculptures.

THE FRENCH REVOLUTION

No. 109 - Thermidor - The Directory. Between the windows, excellent portrait by Jean-Louis La Neuville of *Jules-François Paré*, a somewhat insignificant figure who held the position of Minister of the Interior from 1791 to 1794. The main display cabinet situated at the entrance to the room concerns first of all an historical landmark, 9 Thermidor year II (27th July 1794); the three days that ensued saw the downfall and execution of Robespierre and his leading supporters; this was followed by the "Thermidorian" period, marking the end of the Terror and a return to relative freedom, although the Convention still had to face a number of riots. The various events are illustrated for the most part by prints but also by Hubert Robert's painting *Monument provisoire érigé aux Tuileries lors du transfert des cendres de Jean-Jacques Rousseau d'Ermenonville au Panthéon* in 1794; this night scene shows the extent to which the Revolution revered the famous philosopher.

The other large display cabinet deals with the Directory. Under this régime, between October 1795 and November 1799, the Revolution wallowed in bankruptcy and corruption, and power struggles between the authorities set up by the Constitution of year III were rife. Meanwhile, however, the nouveaux-riches flaunted their luxury and military campaigns brought nothing but success. Portraits of two of the "directors", *La Révellière-Lépeaux*, by Madame Pilastre, after François Gérard, and *Gohier*, by Jacques-Auguste Pajou. Prints relating the main events taking place in Paris during this period, until the coup d'état of 18 and 19 Brumaire year VII (9th and 10th November 1799), which saw power handed over to General Bonaparte, the setting-up of the Consulate and the end of the Revolution.

Drum from the revolutionary wars

No. 110 - The War. The Revolution started out peacefully enough, but from 1792 onwards, it was constantly at war with other European powers while trying to cope at the same time with powerful uprisings by peasant and noble forces in Western France, which were ruthlessly quelled. *Enseigne d'un bureau de recrutement,* polychrome wooden figure wearing the uniform of the National Guard. Pictures conveying the patriotic spirit rekindled by the wars of the Revolution: *Sacrifice à la Patrie,* anon.; *Départ du Volontaire,* anon.; *Chanteurs patriotes,* by Joseph Doncre. Painted portraits of generals: *Marceau,* by Leprince, *Hoche,* anon.; *Servan,* by Louis Lafitte; *Turreau* the Vendée "peacemaker", attributed to Louis Hersent; *Kléber,* anon.; *Augereau,* by Johannes Heinsius; *Un commissaire des guerres,* possibly Pascalis, by Jacques Wilbaut; *Dufriche-Desgenettes,* anon. Charles-Louis Corbet's bust of *Bonaparte* shows the general during the Directory period, as he was beginning to rise in political circles. In the two display cabinets, swords of honour. Drums in the corners of the room.

No. 111 - Vandalism and conservation. This room deals first of all with the harm done to France's architectural heritage under the Revolution, with the wanton destruction of religious buildings in particular, either through fanaticism or more often because of negligence or a taste for easy profit. Paintings by Hubert Robert: *Violation des caveaux royaux à l'église abbatiale de Saint-Denis,* in October 1793; *Démolition de l'église des Feuillants, rue Saint-Honoré; Démolition de l'église Saint-Jean en Grève,* which was situated behind the Hôtel de Ville - this also inspired a painting by Pierre-Antoine de Machy. Amidst all this looting and pillaging, one man devoted himself to saving France's artistic legacy,

THE FRENCH REVOLUTION

Sèvres porcelain

Pierre-Etienne Le Sueur. Plantation d'un arbre de la Liberté.

Alexandre Lenoir, seen here alongside his wife, both portraits painted by Geneviève Bouliard. He founded the Musée des Monuments français in the former Petits-Augustins convent, today the Ecole des Beaux-Arts, using bits of architecture and sculpture seized from the demolition workers;

There are several views of this ephemeral institution, painted by Lubin Vauzelle, Léon Cocherau, etc.;

L'Elysée, dedicated to great men, a garden designed by Lenoir in the same museum, small picture by Hubert Robert.

The Revolution turned the former church of Sainte-Geneviève into the Pantheon, in order to house the remains of the great; this is the subject of a painting attributed to Louis-Léopold Boilly.

No. 112 - Le Sueur. This small room is entirely devoted to the work of Pierre-Etienne Le Sueur, a little-known artist, with a collection of 50 gouaches by him. The brightly-coloured figures, cut out and pasted on a sky-blue background, are imbued with the popular imagery of the time. The artist added his own captions, creating a kind of illustrated journal of the Revolution, recounted in a wonderfully lively manner from beginning to end. Of particular interest are scenes of the mob being harangued at the Palais-Royal on 12th July 1789; a small-scale model of the Bastille (similar to the one in room 102) being carried shoulder-high during a procession; the patriots swearing their oath on Federation Day; a club for women; divorce; a tree of liberty being planted; the September massacres; Bonaparte's dream, etc.

THE VISIT CONTINUES ON THE GROUND-FLOOR, WHICH CAN BE REACHED BY LIFT OR STAIRS (No. 114)

No. 113 - In the display cabinet, collection of Sèvres porcelain, with revolutionary emblems and allegories.

PARIS IN THE FIRST HALF OF THE XIXth CENTURY, FROM THE CONSULATE TO THE SECOND REPUBLIC

No. 115 - The First Empire. The large room opening on to the former garden is devoted to the intermediary political period formed by the Consulate, which followed the coup d'état of 18 Brumaire, and to the imperial régime set up by Napoleon Ist following his consecration in Notre-Dame de Paris on 2nd December 1804. Here, however, we are more concerned with the distant reverberations of the war on Parisian civilian life and society than with

Baron
François Gérard.
Madame Récamier

the Napoleonic wars themselves. Full-length portrait of
Napoléon Ier, painted in 1809 by Robert Lefèvre. On the right
of the portrait, in the display cabinet, Napoleon's campaign
kit, including a great many items in silver gilt which all fit
perfectly into an astutely-fashioned fitted chest made by
Biennais. In the left-hand display cabinet: Napoleon's
breastplate of honour and a pair of his horse pistols; bronze
cast of his death mask made in Sainte-Hélène. Full-length
portrait of *Charles-Maurice de Talleyrand-Périgord*, painted in
1808 by Pierre-Paul Prud'hon, master of the art of
chiaroscuro; the illustrious statesman, as intelligent as he was
cynical, is seen here dressed up as Lord Chamberlain of the
Empire. Portrait of *Madame Récamier*, painted in 1805 by the
baron François Gérard who surpassed himself in this famous
picture, which captures so well the model's grace and beauty
in the full bloom of youth; Juliette Récamier had just turned
down the portrait she had commissioned from David, which
remained in draft form and is now in the Louvre. Two other
beauties of Imperial society life are portrayed: *Mademoiselle
Duchesnois* of the Comédie-Française, by the same artist, and
Madame Hamelin, by Andrea Appiani. Bust of Pope *Pie VII*
by Louis-Pierre Deseine, recalling his visit to Paris for the
Imperial consecration.

Opposite the windows, paintings with a narrative
theme: *Cortège du sacre de Napoléon* going over the Pont-
Neuf, by Jacques Bertaux; *Bénédiction des drapeaux devant
Notre-Dame*, attributed to Antoine Gros; *Conscrits de 1807
défilant devant la porte Saint-Denis*, by Louis-Léopold Boilly,
one of the artist's best works in its meticulous and
unemotional rendering of the effect of the Imperial campaigns
on Paris. He is also responsible for a grisaille imitation

PARIS IN THE FIRST HALF OF THE XIXth CENTURY,
FROM THE CONSULATE TO THE SECOND REPUBLIC

Item from Napoleon 1st's campaign kit

engraving, *Galeries du palais du tribunat* (Palais-Royal). Two
paintings by Etienne Bouhot show the Empire's achievements
in the field of architecture and town planning: *Place du
Châtelet* with its Palmier fountain; the original lead statue
from this fountain, representing la Renommée, by the sculptor
Boizot, is now in the garden of the hôtel Carnavalet; *Place
Vendôme* and its column, erected in honour of the Grande
Armée, with the rue de la Paix, opened up during that
period. In the middle of the room is a lamp in bronze gilt
which used to belong to the maréchal Suchet, duc d'Albufera.

No. 116 - The Restoration. A painting by Jean
Zippel, the *Entrée des souverains alliés à Paris*, on the Grands
Boulevards in 1814, evokes the fall of the Empire caused by
Napoleon's reversal of fortune on the military front. The
constitutional monarchy is embodied by its two successive
sovereigns, *Louis XVIII* and *Charles X* : the first is portrayed
by Robert Lefèvre, the second by François Gérard. *Allégorie
en l'honneur de la Restauration*, a painting by Pierre-Nicolas
Legrand. The total mastery of Louis-Léopold Boilly's art is
illustrated in the *Distribution de vin et de comestibles aux
Champs-Elysées* for the King's birthday in 1822. *Mort du duc
de Berry*, painting by François Cibot: the heir of the elder
branch of the Bourbons was stabbed by Louvel on 13th

February 1820 as he was entering the Opera. Bronze statue of his posthumous son Henri, *Duc de Bordeaux*, by Philippe-Joseph Lemaire, later comte de Chambord. Lancelot Turpin de Crissé's painting, *Messe à la Chapelle Expiatoire*, records the heartfelt worship expressed in memory of Louis XVI. Large inlaid roll top desk, the work of the cabinet maker François-Laurent Puteaux.

Nos. 117 and 118 - The painters' view of Paris (1800-1850). The museum owns an impressive collection of XIXth century views of Paris. It is worth noting that the

Martin Drolling.
Eglise Saint-Eustache
vue d'un atelier
d'artiste

PARIS IN THE FIRST HALF OF THE XIXth CENTURY, FROM THE CONSULATE TO THE SECOND REPUBLIC

artists were generally more interested in the picturesque aspects of the city than in the transformations taking place in the fields of architecture and town planning, but admittedly these were on a limited scale until the advent of the Second Empire.

The first room houses the most ancient pictures (Empire and Restoration), viewed from an objective and scrupulously realistic standpoint, in the tradition of the previous two centuries of urban painting. Works by Etienne Bouhot *(Tuileries vues du quai d'Orsay)*, James Chalon *(Marché et la fontaine des Innocents)*, Hippolyte Adam, Lina Jaunez *(Ruines de Saint-Louis, du Louvre et de l'hôtel de Longueville)*, etc. Painting attributed to Martin Drolling: *Eglise Saint-Eustache vue d'un atelier d'artiste*. In the display cabinet, porcelain from the same period, decorated with views of Paris.

J.A. Regnier (1787-1860). La voûte du quai de Guevres

Most of the pictures exhibited in the second room are contemporary with the July monarchy. The works of an Italian painter, Giuseppe Canella (*Le Pont-Neuf, Marché aux fleurs,* etc.) are typical of the unemotional and minute attention to detail shown by the specialists of urban views, equally displayed in Isidore Dagnan's *Boulevard Poissonnière*; but romantic inspiration creeps in with Georges Michel's *Paysage au moulin*, and Camille Corot's personal and subtle brand of poetry is apparent in *Quai des Orfèvres* and one of his rare view of Paris, *Pont Saint-Michel.*

No. 119 - July 1830. The museum is richly endowed with iconographical accounts of the days known as the "Trois Glorieuses", sparked off by the four rulings of 25th July, which put an end to the reign of Charles X and saw the younger branch of the Bourbons accede in turn to the throne. Scenes of the uprising, which was virtually limited to Paris, by Hippolyte Lecomte, Jean-Louis Bezard, etc. Scale model by Foulley showing the duc d'Orléans arriving place de l'Hôtel de Ville to be proclaimed lieutenant general of the kingdom before becoming King Louis-Philippe. Small-scale bronze model of the *Colonne de Juillet*, the work of the architect Alavoine, which was erected place de la Bastille in honour of the victims of the uprising.

PARIS IN THE FIRST HALF OF THE XIXth CENTURY, FROM THE CONSULATE TO THE SECOND REPUBLIC

No. 120 - The July monarchy. Anonymous painting of the *Duc d'Orléans devant la foule place du Châtelet.* Anonymous bronze bust of *Louis-Philippe, roi des Français,* and remarkable carved marble bust of Queen *Marie-Amélie* by Antonin Moine. Louis-Philippe's large roll top desk, badly chipped during the looting of the Tuileries in 1848. In one of the display cabinets, sword of honour of the comte de Paris, the King's grandson. Pictures illustrating the more glorious aspects of the régime : *Erection de l'obélisque de Louqsor sur la Place de la Concorde* on 25th October 1836 by François Dubois ; large painting by Geslin showing the transformations this occasioned, based on designs by Hittorff ; Karl Girardet's *Tente du chef de l'armée marocaine exposée au jardin des*

Pierre Louis Foulley. Scale model showing. L'Arrivée sur la place de l'Hôtel de Ville du duc d'Orléans on 31st July 1830

Tuileries; lively sketch of *le Banquet des dames aux Tuileries* by the famous architect Eugène Viollet Le Duc. Large scale model of the *Galeries d'Orléans,* built in the Palais-Royal gardens before Louis-Philippe's accession to the throne : only the colonades remain today. Another scale model depicting the *Attentat de Fieschi* in the boulevard du Temple on 28th July 1835 ; small anonymous picture on the same theme. Painting by Jacques-Raymond Brascassat showing the *Tête de Fieschi,* following the trial and execution of the author of this attempt on Louis-Philippe's life. In one of the display cabinets, a plaster-cast sculpture by François Rude, *Départ des Volontaires,* a rough draft of the famous haut-relief featured on the Arc de Triomphe.

PARIS IN THE FIRST HALF OF THE XIXth CENTURY,
FROM THE CONSULATE TO THE SECOND REPUBLIC

No. 121 - The Second Republic. Paintings by
Hagnauer, Tonny Johannot, Eugène Gabe, Joseph Felon,
etc., retracing the major events of the famous days in
February 1848, which brought the July monarchy to an end,
and illustrating the workers' revolt against the Republic's
interim government in June of the same year. Sketch painted
by Félix Philippoteaux of *Lamartine repoussant le drapeau
rouge sur le perron de l'Hôtel de Ville*. Victor Baltard's plaster
scale model of the *Monument funéraire de Monseigneur Affre*,
archbishop of Paris, killed in June on the barricades while
attempting to pacify the opposing forces. Portraits of
politicians and socialist thinkers who played a part in the
events : *Ledru Rollin*, by Joséphine Mongez; the worker
Albert, member of the interim government, by Joseph Navlet;
Eugène Blanqui, by Amélie Serre; *Proudhon*, artist unknown;
Louis Blanc, by Pierre Dupuis. Suite of small paintings by
Jean-Jacques Champin on the theme of celebrations and
ceremonies of the Second Republic. Ernest Pichio's painting
of *Victor Baudin sur une barricade du faubourg Saint-Antoine*,
on 3rd December 1851; this deputy was one of the few
Republican figures to take up arms against the coup d'état
organized the day before by Prince-President Louis-Napoléon
Bonaparte; he was shot dead on the barricades.

No. 122 - The Romantic movement. The museum
is richly endowed with portraits, in painted or sculpted form,
of the writers, actors and actresses, composers, singers,
painters and other personalities from the world of art and
literature who turned Paris into one of the centres of the
Romantic movement. A painting of *Franz Liszt* by Henri
Lehmann, a German disciple of Ingres, represents one of the
best portraits of the illustrious Hungarian composer and

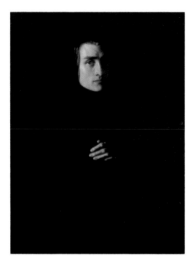

Henri Lehmann.
Portrait
of Franz Liszt

virtuoso, who spent a large part of his cosmopolitan life in Paris. His muse and companion, *Marie d'Agoult*, is shown here portrayed by the same artist. Portraits of the famous opera-singers Félicité Garcia, otherwise known as la *Malibran*, by Henri Decaisne, and *Marietta Alboni*, by Alexis-Joseph Pérignon; portrait of the great historian *Jules Michelet* by Thomas Couture. Round inlaid table made by Puteaux for Charles Xth's consecration. Large inlaid bookcase by the same cabinet maker, decorated with lions' heads. On the shelves are small plaster and bronze sculptures by Jean-Pierre Dantan, who devoted his art to the famous men and women of the time - politicians, writers, musicians, actors, artists, figures from high society - depicted in miniature bust form, often amusingly caricatured; among the most remarkable of these are Talleyrand, Rossini, Liszt and Paganini.

THE VISITOR CROSSES THE MAIN STAIRCASE (No. 123), BUT REMAINS ON THE GROUND FLOOR

PARIS IN THE FIRST HALF OF THE XIXth CENTURY,
FROM THE CONSULATE TO THE SECOND REPUBLIC

Nos. 124 and 125 - The Romantic movement (contd.). The first of these two small rooms is devoted to portraits of writers : *Lamartine*, by an unknown artist, and *Lamartine* again, by his wife ; *Victor Hugo*, by François Heim ; *Alfred de Vigny* dressed in the uniform of a young policeman of the King's household, attributed to François Kinson ; the brothers *Paul et Alfred de Musset* as children, by Fortuné Dufau ; *Théophile Gautier*, by Auguste de Chatillon. Charles-Emile de Champmartin's portrait of the painter *Eugène Delacroix*. Canvas by Albertini : *Exposition des œuvres de Delacroix*. In the display cabinets of both rooms, mementœs of writers (Lamartine), actors and actresses (Talma, Rachel).

The next room gives an idea of Parisian life during the Romantic period, particularly through street scenes. *Descente de la Courtille*, the popular annual fête in the rue de Belleville, paintings by Charles Nanteuil and Jean Pezous. *Scènes de carnaval* place de la Concorde, by Ernest Seigneurgens and Eugène Lami, and on the Pont-Neuf, by Guillaume Romny.

THE VISITOR RETRACES HIS STEPS AND CLIMBS THE MAIN STAIRCASE (No. 123) TO THE FIRST FLOOR.

This beautiful late XVIIth century staircase, designed by Pierre Bullet, is one of the only two remaining items of interior decoration in the house. Note the banister, an exceptional piece of work in cast iron.

ONCE ON THE FIRST FLOOR LANDING, THE VISITOR TURNS RIGHT

Nos. 126 and 127 - The painters' view of Paris
(contd.). These two small rooms are complementary with
rooms 117 and 118, showing a number of views of the capital
during the Romantic period. Quite a few English painters
visited Paris at that time, bringing with them a taste for bright
colours, as can be seen in Robert Stanley's *Boulevard des
Capucines*, William Parrott's *Institut* and *Paris vu de
Montmartre*, by George Arnold. They also left their mark on
the views of Théodore Gudin and Charles Mozin and were not
without influence on Louis Daguerre's romantically inspired
work - although it is true that his name is more readily
associated with the art of photography - not to mention Paul
Huet, Eugène Ciceri, Antoine Vollon...A more traditional
brand of realism reappears, however, in works such as
Première gare Saint-Lazare, an anonymous painting evoking
the advent of the railway in Paris.

The second room also houses a pair of concave
models for the half-domes of the main room of the Sénat,
painted by Henri Lehmann, allegorically representing *La
France sous les Mérovingiens et les Capétiens* and *La France
sous les Valois et les Bourbons.*

THE VISITOR RETRACES HIS STEPS AND CROSSES THE UPPER LANDING OF
THE STAIRCASE (No. 123), WHERE HE CAN SEE TWO VAST *VUES
PANORAMIQUES DE PARIS* CIRCA 1852, BY VICTOR NAVLET, AND A
FRAGMENT OF THE *PANORAMA DE PARIS*, A WORK BY ALFRED STEVENS
AND HENRI GERVEX, WHICH IS UNFORTUNATELY NO LONGER IN ONE PIECE

PARIS FROM THE SECOND EMPIRE TO THE PRESENT DAY

No. 128 - The Second Empire. The works of art displayed in this room illustrate some of the aspects of political, society and court life under the Imperial régime set up by Louis-Napoléon Bonaparte, who reigned as Napoléon III from 1852 to 1870. Anonymous painting of the *Fête au Champ de Mars* on 10th May 1852 : the Prince-President was not officially Emperor at the time, but certainly gave the impression that he was. *Arrivée de la reine Victoria à la gare de l'Est* for the 1855 universal exhibition, artist unknown. By Emmanuel Massé, *Les troupes défilant sur les Grands Boulevards à leur retour de Crimée* in December 1855. Pierre Tetar Van Elven's *Fête de nuit aux Tuileries* in honour of the 1867 universal exhibition. *L'allée des Feuillants aux Tuileries*, thronged with elegant passers-by, anon. Painting by Henri Béroud, *L'escalier du nouvel Opéra*. *Berceau d'apparat* given to Napoléon III and Empress Eugénie in 1856 by the Ville de Paris on the birth of their son, the Imperial Prince : this magnificent work of art was largely created by the goldsmith Froment-Meurice, working from designs by the architect Victor Baltard, and includes enamels painted after Hippolyte Flandrin and silver figures based on the models of the sculptor Pierre Simart. Life at court is conjured up by the busts of Albert-Ernest Carrier-Belleuse, representing the Emperor's favourites, *Marguerite Bellanger*, the *Comtesse de Castiglione*, etc. Portrait in pastel by Simon Rochard of the writer and very first inspector of Historical Monuments, *Prosper Mérimée*. A large canvas by Adolphe Yvon introduces a more serious note in its depiction of an episode in municipal history and official life : *Napoléon III signant en 1859 le décret d'annexion à la Ville de Paris des communes urbaines* (Vaugirard, Montmartre, Belleville, etc...) ; portrait

The Imperial Prince's cradle

Canella.
Rue de la Paix

of *Baron Haussmann*, prefect of the Seine and the driving
force behind all the major transformations in the capital,
attributed to Henri Lehmann.

A few tragic events also cast a shadow over the
Second Empire in Paris, such as the *Attentat d'Orsini* on 14th
January 1858, the subject of a painting by H. Vittori.

No. 129 - The Second Empire (contd.). Large
relief scale model by Foulley representing the *Défilé de
l'armée d'Italie sur la Place Vendôme* in 1859. This small
room is mainly concerned, however, with the architecture of
the Second Empire and the vast town planning programme
which reshaped and modernized Paris, often to the detriment
of its monumental heritage and its more picturesque aspects.
Canvases by minor artists show the levelling-down of the butte
de Chaillot, the opening of the avenue de l'Opéra, Garnier's
Opera House, the Auteuil viaduct, the church of La Trinité,
etc., and also a panoramic view of the *Exposition universelle
de 1867* by a certain Lami.

PARIS FROM THE SECOND EMPIRE
TO THE PRESENT DAY

No. 130 - The siege of Paris. The serious change of fortune experienced by France in her war against Prussia, which had begun in 1870, led to the fall of the Empire and the restoration of the Republic : *Proclamation de la déchéance de Napoléon III devant le palais du Corps Législatif* (Palais Bourbon) on 4th September 1870, a large canvas by Jules Didier and Jacques Guiaud. But the country was invaded and Paris, under siege from 1870 to 1871, found itself facing shelling and tremendous hardship. Several paintings by the same artists and by Alfred Decaen convey these tragic times, the most important of which is *Départ en ballon de Gambetta depuis Montmartre*. In an unusual work, Camille Corot imagines *Paris incendié*. The Parisians did not lose hope, however, as can be seen from Pierre Puvis de Chavannes' two sketches for the fine allegorical figures, *Ballon* and *Pigeon voyageur*.

No. 131 - The Commune. The workers' uprising in 1871, which was crushed by the Versailles government, sparked off meetings, fighting, executions without trial and widespread destruction, as shown in several pictures by minor artists, the most remarkable being Théobald Chartran's *Monseigneur Darboy sur son lit de mort*; the archbishop of Paris was killed while a hostage at the hands of the Communards. Portraits of some leading figures in the Commune : the writer *Jules Vallès*, by Gustave Courbet ; *Louise Michel*, the revolutionary, by Louis Tinayre. A *vue du Louvre avec les Tuileries incendiées*, by Siebe Ten Cate, recalls the havoc wreaked in Paris by a Commune in its death throes.

No. 132 - The Third Republic (1872 to 1914). A rather dull period iconographically speaking. Several pictures are worth noting, however, such as the portraits of the journalist *Henri Rochefort*, by Baud-Bovy, the politician *Waldeck-Rousseau* by Henri Gervex, and another of *General Boulanger* by J. Williamson.

No. 133 - The painters' view of Paris (2nd half of XIXth century). This is essentially a collection of works by minor artists, in keeping with the tradition of topographically accurate observation, such as Emmanuel Lansyer and Victor Dargaud, the author of a curious little painting, *La Statue de la Liberté de New York dans l'atelier de fonderie Gayet-Gauthier, rue de Chazelles*, in 1884; Bartholdi's colossal copper-plate figure was indeed temporarily erected in Paris before being dismantled and sent to New York.

No. 134 - Sitting-room. This white- and gold-panelled room is typical of the late Louis XIV style and is the only original item of interior decoration still in existence, apart from the main staircase.

No. 135 - The painters' view of Paris (2nd half of XIXth century contd.). Like their predecessors, the artists of this period were generally more interested in a traditionally picturesque view of Paris than in the contributions of architecture and town planning. The delicate brushstroke of Stanislas Lepine *(La Seine vue du pont d'Austerlitz)* marks the transition between his master Corot and the Impressionists, who are represented here, in quality rather than quantity, alongside other artists who painted in a similar vein or carried on the movement into neo-Impressionism : *La rue et l'église Saint-Séverin*, by Jongkind; *La Seine vue de Bercy*, by Armand Guillaumin; Albert Lebourg's *Trocadéro vu de la Seine*; *Moulins à Montmartre* in 1884, by Paul Signac, an early work reminiscent of Van Gogh in its bold brushstrokes and vivacious hues; Maximilien Luce's *La Cité à la tête du pont*

PARIS FROM THE SECOND EMPIRE
TO THE PRESENT DAY

Saint-Michel around 1803. Next to these paintings hang works by lesser-known, more eclectic artists, whose art claims to be Realist despite a certain Impressionist influence : Jean-Baptiste Guillemet, Luigi Loir, Siebe Ten Cate, Frank Boggs, Lucien Lévy-Dhurmer, Jean-François Raffaelli, Marie-François Firmin-Girard.

Jean Béraud. Les coulisses de l'Opéra

No. 136 - The world of literature. This was a time of great brilliance in literary and entertainment circles, evoked in the museum's large collection of portraits of writers and theatrical personalities, which also includes some of their personal possessions. There are paintings of the *Comtesse de Ségur, Alphonse Daudet, François Coppée, Victorien Sardou* and his family in their drawing-room, by Auguste de la Brély, a small portrait of *Paul Verlaine* by F.A. Cazals, the brothers *Coquelin*, both actors (bust of the younger by Antoine Bourdelle), *Mounet-Sully* and *Sarah Bernardt.* Three statuettes by Cappiello of well-known names from less illustrious forms of entertainment, *Jeanne Granier, Réjane* and *Yvette Guilbert,* seen here in action.

Nos. 137 and 138 - The Belle Epoque. Despite ups and downs and shadows on the political horizon, the last quarter of the XIXth century and the very first years of the XXth were epitomised in Paris by a sense of carefree exuberance in which entertainment of all kinds and society events flourished. The feel of the "Belle Epoque" was acutely conveyed by Jean Béraud, an accurate, if slightly ironic observer, whose thirty or so pictures adorn the first of these two rooms. This is the largest public collection of his works. Among the many scenes of entertainment, restaurants and cafés, luxury boutiques, race-meetings and society events, several particularly lively views of the Grands Boulevards

THE VISITOR CLIMBS THE SPIRAL STAIRCASE TO THE MEZZANINE

stand out: *la Soirée, la Colonne Morris, Au jardin de Paris.*

The second room is devoted to the same aspects of Parisian life, interpreted by other painters: Giuseppe de Nittis, Jean-Louis Forain *(Une loge de théâtre)*, André Gill *(Sur le boulevard)*, Maurice Delondre *(Dans l'omnibus)*, Edmond Grandjean *(La place de Clichy)*, Georges Stein *(L'avenue du Bois)*, Alfred Smith *(Les courses d'Auteuil).*

PARIS FROM THE SECOND EMPIRE
TO THE PRESENT DAY

No. 139 - Upper landing. Series of paintings by
Emile Guillier, unknown outside the Carnavalet museum,
whose inspiration is a cross between Realism and
Impressionism.

No. 140 - Lower landing. Items of "Belle Epoque"
décor: stained glass windows from the famous cabaret "Le
Chat Noir", two mosaic figures based on sketches by Jean-
Louis Forain, originally in the Café Riche.

**THE VISITOR GOES BACK
DOWN THE SPIRAL
STAIRCASE TO THE
FIRST FLOOR**

No. 141 - The Café de Paris. The private room
shown here was designed in 1899 by Henri Sauvage for the
famous café established in the avenue de l'Opéra; the purity
of its interior decoration is a valuable example of "Art
Nouveau", like the following ensemble:

No. 142 - Fouquet's jewellery shop. The
outstanding décor of this luxurious jewellery shop in the rue
Royale has been reassembled here (and in room 143).
Alphonse Mucha was entirely responsible for the design of
this work of art, which was executed by skilled craftsmen.

No. 143 - Fouquet's shop window.

No. 144 - Corridor. Several pictures depicting
major construction work in Paris around 1900. Public
conveniences.

No. 145 - The Great War (1914-1918). The aim
here is not to portray the battles of the First World War as
such, but to illustrate the repercussions of the war on Paris,
which could be quite dramatic: *La voûte de l'église Saint-
Gervais écroulée* following a blast from a "Big Bertha" shell
(29th March 1918). Most of the paintings are concerned with
the ceremonies and celebrations held to mark the armistice
and victory: *Réception des maréchaux Joffre et Foch à la porte
Maillot* on 14th July 1919, by Lucien Simon.

**Alphonse Mucha.
Fouquet's
jewellery shop**

Henri Sauvage.
The Café de Paris.

PARIS FROM THE SECOND EMPIRE
TO THE PRESENT DAY

No. 146 - Ballroom of the hôtel de Wendel. This vast and opulent décor was created in 1924 by the Catalan painter Jose Maria Sert y Badia, one of the leading lights in the Paris of the "années folles". His flamboyant sense of the baroque was allowed to run free in the lacquered, white-gold wall panels, which merge into a coved ceiling painted on canvas, on the theme of the *Cortège de la Reine de Saba*.

No. 147 - The world of literature in the XIXth century. The focal point of this room is an ensemble of furniture and personal mementoes belonging to three writers, *Paul Léautaud*, the illustrious *Marcel Proust* and the poetess

Jose Maria Sert.
Ballroom of the
Hôtel de Wendel

Evocation of
Marcel
Proust's bedroom

THE VISITOR GOES PAST
THE FOOT OF STAIRCASE
No. 100 ONCE MORE AND
ENTERS GALLERY 148,
LINKING THE TWO
MANSIONS

Anna de Noailles, who all shared the habit of writing in bed. Among the other portraits hanging in this room: *Georges Courteline*, by Léopold Stevens; *La Comtesse de Noailles*, by Jean-Louis Forain; Comtesse Greffulhe's pastel of *Abbé Mugnier*, renowned for his contacts in high society; the writers *Jean Cocteau* and *René Crevel*, by Jacques-Emile Blanche; the scholar *Jean Rostand*, by Léonard Foujita; the dress designer *Paul Poiret*, by Paul Guillaume; *Juliette Gréco*, by Robert Humblot.

No. 148 - The painters' view of Paris in the XXth century. Rather than adopt a systematic approach to the

PARIS FROM THE SECOND EMPIRE
TO THE PRESENT DAY

subject, the works displayed in this gallery have been selected in order to illustrate the variety of movements and trends, naturally excluding non-figurative art, which have characterized the evolution of painting in Paris since approximately 1920 : Realism in Jules Adler *(Les premières communiantes)*, late neo-Impressionism in Maximilien Luce *(Construction du pont du Carrousel)* and Paul Signac *(Le pont des Arts)*, an attenuated version of Fauvism in Albert Marquet *(Notre-Dame sous la neige)*, Marcel Gromaire's nod to Cubism *(La place Blanche)*, independent Realism in Maurice Utrillo *(Saint-Pierre de Montmartre et le Sacré-Cœur)*, a blend of traditional Japanese art and the spirit of "l'école de Paris" in Léonard Foujita's work *(L'hôtel Edgar Quinet, Intérieur d'un bistrot)*. Paris seen through the eyes of contemporary artists, such as Benn, Oguiss, Serge Belloni, Sergio Telles, Kojiro Akagi…

Paul Signac.
Le pont des Arts

THE GALLERY LEADS
DIRECTLY INTO THE
HOTEL CARNAVALET
AND THE EXIT IS
SITUATED AT THE FOOT
OF THE STAIRS

Paul Signac.
Moulins
de Montmartre

Practical information

VISITORS' ENTRANCE

23, rue de Sévigné, 75003 Paris.

HOURS OF OPENING

Tuesday to Sunday, 10.00 to 17.40. Closed on Mondays.

TRANSPORT

métros Saint-Paul, Chemin Vert, Bastille, Hôtel-de-Ville.
bus Nos. 29,69,76,96.

INFORMATION FOR VISITORS

Key-in data facility on the French Revolution (1st floor of the
Hôtel Le Peletier de Saint-Fargeau).
Key-in data facility on the museum's collections (ground floor
of the Hôtel Carnavalet). Illustrated guides and brochures on
sale in the bookshop.

COMMUNICATIONS AND ACTIVITY CENTRE

Conferences, workshops, educational visits, concerts. Information regarding temporary exhibitions.

AMIS DU MUSEE CARNAVALET

Information and enrolment at the association's desk (entrance situated in the main courtyard, 23, rue de Sévigné).

THE "PARIS MUSEES" BOUTIQUE

Offers a range of products created by "Paris Musées", many of which are inspired by the collections of the Carnavalet museum.

THE "PARIS MUSEES" BOOKSHOP

Offers a wide choice of books, catalogues, albums and publications on the theme of Paris and its history.

DOCUMENTATION SECTIONS

The Graphic Arts room is open to authorized researchers and professionals from Tuesday to Friday, 14.00 to 17.30, and by appointment for items held in the Reserves (entrance 29, rue de Sévigné).

The phototheque of the Musées de la Ville de Paris (entrance 29, rue de Sévigné) is open from 10.00 to 12.00 and from 14.00 to 17.00.

Reproductions of works of art belonging to the Musées de la Ville de Paris available on receipt of order.

CURATORS' DEPARTMENT, GRAPHIC ARTS ROOM, PHOTOTHEQUE

29, rue de Sévigné, 75003 Paris.
Tel. : 42 72 21 13

Photoengraving Pragmaphot - **Typesetting** L'Union Linotypiste - **First printed** by Imprimerie L'Alençonnaise in January 1990 - Registration of copyright first quarter 1990 - ISBN 2-901414-39.7 - **Editor** Bernard de Montgolfier - **Editing supervisors** Brigitte de Montclos and Sixtine de Naurois - **Production manager** Gilles Beaujard - **Graphic design** Hervé Ollitraut-Bernard assisted by Sylvie Jamilloux-Biehler - **Technical advisor** Arnauld Pontier - **English translation** Caroline Taylor-Bouché. Copyright Ville de Paris by Spadem, plates from the phototheque of the Musées de la Ville de Paris: Irène Andreani, Marc Dubroca, Didier Giet, Olivier Habouzi, Denis Schwarz, photographers of the Musées de la Ville de Paris.